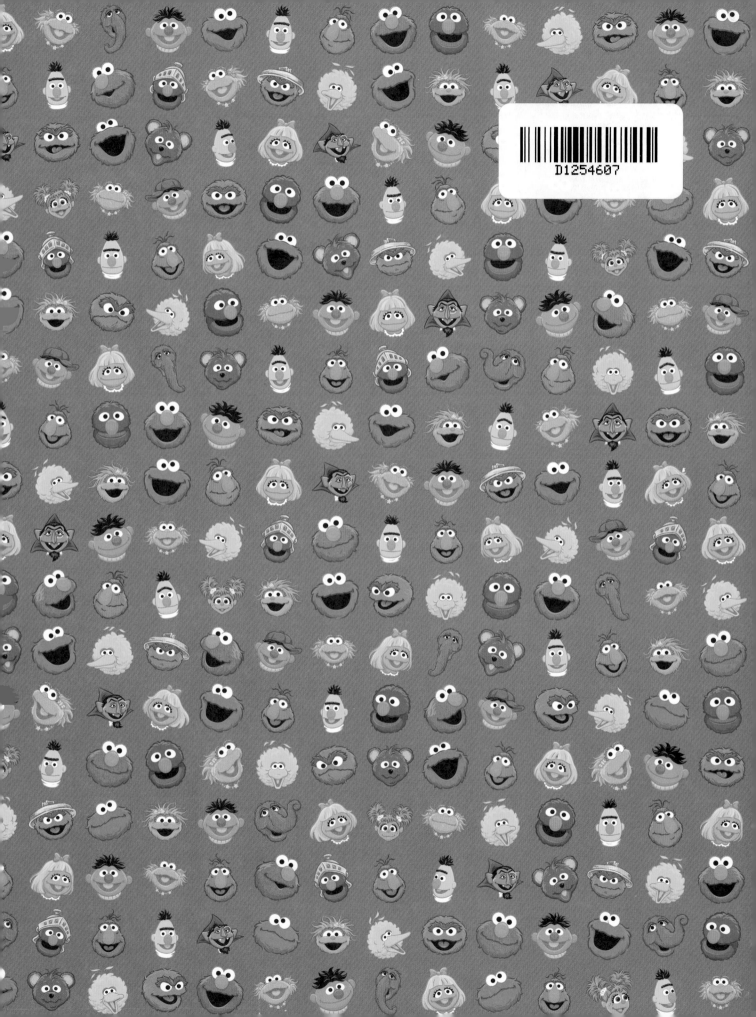

# First

# Crafts

First published by Parragon in 2009

Parragon
Queen Street House
4 Queen Street
Bath BA1 1HE, UK

ISBN 978-1-4075-7198-0

Printed in China

# 123 SESAME STREET®

# First Crafts

## PaRragon

Bath  New York  Singapore  Hong Kong  Cologne  Delhi  Melbourne

# TIPS FOR SUCCESS

## Prepare your space

Cover your workspace with newspaper or a plastic or paper tablecloth. Make sure you and your children are wearing clothes (including shoes!) that you don't mind becoming spattered with food, paint, or glue. But relax! You'll never completely avoid mess; in fact, it's part of the fun!

## Wash your hands

Wash your hands (and your child's hands) before starting a new project, and clean up as you go along. Clean hands make for clean crafts! Remember to wash your hands afterward, too, using soap and warm water to get off any of the remaining materials.

## Follow steps carefully

Follow each step carefully, and in the sequence in which it appears. We've tested all the projects; we know they work, and we want them to work for you, too. Also, ask your children, if they are old enough, to read along with you as you work through the steps. For a younger child, you can direct her to look at the pictures on the page to try to guess what the next step is.

## Measure precisely

If a project gives you measurements, use your ruler, T-square, measuring cups, or measuring spoons to make sure you measure as accurately as you can. Sometimes the success of the project may depend on it. Also, this is a great opportunity to teach measuring techniques to your child.

## Be patient

You may need to wait while something bakes or leave paint, glue, or clay to dry, sometimes for a few hours or even overnight. Encourage your child to be patient as well; explain to her why she must wait, and, if possible, find ways to entertain her as you are waiting. For example you can show her how long you have to wait by pointing out the time on a clock.

## Clean up

When you've finished your project, clean up any mess. Store all the materials together so that they are ready for the next time you want to craft. Ask your child to help.

# JEWELRY BOX

## YOU WILL NEED

- Box with lid
- Scissors
- Old newspaper
- White glue
- Colored fabric or felt
- Gold paint, glitter, and sequins
- Shiny buttons or craft jewels

Cut the newspaper into squares and glue two layers all over the box and lid. Leave to dry between layers. You could also glue a piece of colored fabric or felt inside the box to line it.

Paint the box and lid inside and out with gold paint. You may need two coats to cover them completely.

When the paint is dry, decorate the lid and sides of the box with glitter, paint, sequins, and recycled buttons or jewels.

**DID YOU KNOW?**
Your gold jewelry is out of this world! Gold was floating around in space before our planet Earth was even formed!

Tie a pretty ribbon around your box to decorate the sides!

## YOU WILL NEED

- Sheet white paper
- Ruler
- Pencil
- Colored paper
- Scissors
- White glue
- Clear contact paper

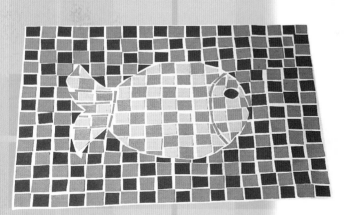

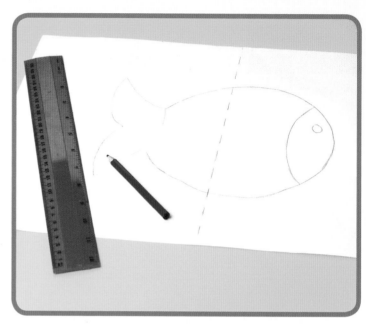

**1**

Begin by drawing a simple outline of a fish, or anything else, on your paper. Make sure that the picture is in the middle.

**2**

Decide which colors you want for your picture, then use a ruler and pencil to measure out lots of small squares on colored paper. Cut them out. Make sure you have plenty of each color.

Elmo made place mats for Elmo's whole family to use at dinnertime!

Glue the squares onto your picture. Begin in the top corner, and work from one side to the other.

4

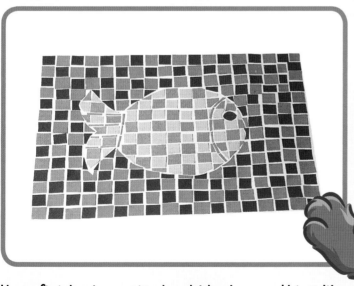

Your finished mosaic should look something like this. To protect it, ask a grown-up to cover it with a layer of clear contact paper.

# FELT JEWELRY

## YOU WILL NEED

- Felt squares: various colors
- Scissors
- Fabric glue
- Rubber band
- Needle and colored embroidery thread
- Polyester stuffing
- Ribbon

Cut three squares of colored felt, each slightly smaller than the last. Layer them, using a little glue to hold them in place.

Now roll the felt up tightly into a sausage, using glue to stick it. You will need to hold the sausage in place with a rubber band while the glue dries.

KIDS

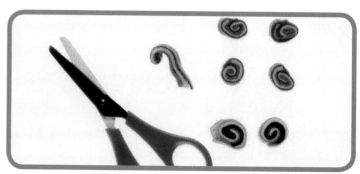

When the glue is thoroughly dry, use scissors to cut the sausage into beads.

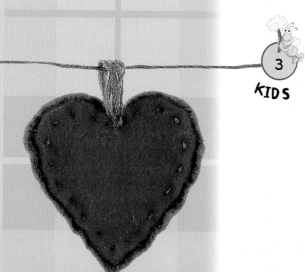

4

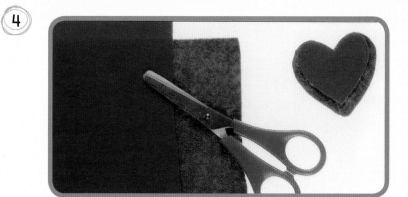

To make a heart pendant, use two squares of colored felt. Cut out a heart from each color, making one smaller than the other.

5

Place a little stuffing between the layers and sew them together with colored thread. Make a ribbon loop at the top for threading.

6

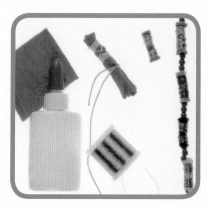

To make these beads, roll a small square of felt. Hold in place with glue, then wind colored thread around it to make decorative bands.

# PICTURE PUZZLES

## YOU WILL NEED

- Picture you have drawn or one from a magazine
- Thin cardboard (same size as your picture)
- White glue
- Ruler
- Pencil
- Scissors

**1 KIDS**

Glue your picture onto a piece of thin cardboard, making sure every part of the picture—even the edges—is firmly glued down.

**2**

Divide the picture into evenly sized pieces with a pencil and ruler. Carefully cut the picture into pieces along the pencil lines.

**3 KIDS**

Jumble up the pieces, then try to complete your picture puzzle.

**4 KIDS**

Keep all the puzzle pieces in an envelope so they don't get lost.

I bet you are a SUPER puzzle-doer!

# FOIL FRAMES

## YOU WILL NEED

- Thick cardboard
- Ruler
- Strong scissors
- Aluminum foil
- Gluestick
- Pencil and ballpoint pen

①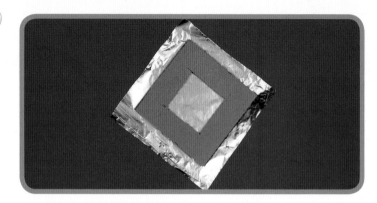

Cut out two cardboard squares, one with a square picture hole in the middle. Cut a foil square an inch larger than the frame.

②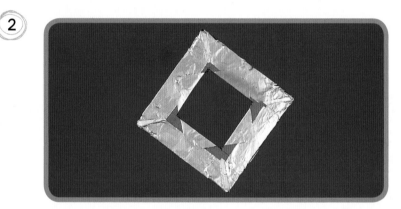

Spread the cardboard frame with glue. With clean fingers, gently press the foil over the frame. Tuck in the edges carefully, and smooth down the foil.

③ KIDS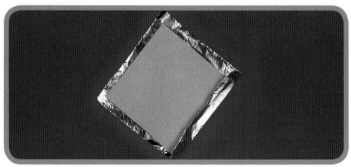

Cover the remaining square with foil. This is the back of the frame.

Attach the frame to the back with glue on three sides, leaving an opening at the top to slip in the photo.

5

KIDS

Use the ballpoint pen to mark a design onto the front of the frame. Don't press too hard or you might tear the foil.

DID YOU KNOW? Aluminum foil can be recycled, so don't throw it away. Put it in a recycling bin!

You can make your frame any shape you like – a square, a rectangle, a circle, even a star!

# TISSUE PAPER CARDS

## YOU WILL NEED

- Colored paper
- Colored tissue paper
- Scissors
- White glue

**1 KIDS**

Fold a piece of colored paper in half to make the card. Tear off pieces of colored tissue paper and glue them onto the card.

**2 KIDS**

Layer on strips of different colored tissue paper, or make a picture using different colors and shapes. When the glue is dry, your card is ready for you to write a special message inside.

To make an eye-catching Valentine card, layer four pieces of red tissue paper together, fold them in half, and tear out a heart shape. Stick the hearts on top of each other in the middle of the card. The border of the card is made from strips of red tissue paper.

MAIL

# MAGIC PICTURES

## YOU WILL NEED

- Thin cardboard or paper: white
- Scissors
- Colored markers
- Clear plastic folder
- Adhesive tape

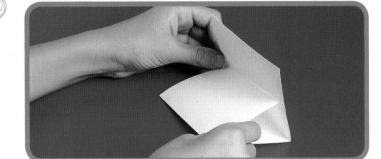

**1**

Take a sheet of thin cardboard or paper and fold it into three equal sections as shown in the picture.

**2**

On the front flap mark out a rectangle and the finger grip space. Cut away the finger grip space.

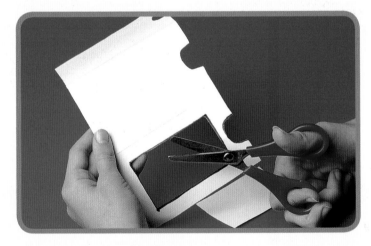

**3**

Open out the cardboard and cut out the rectangle. This is the front frame of the card.

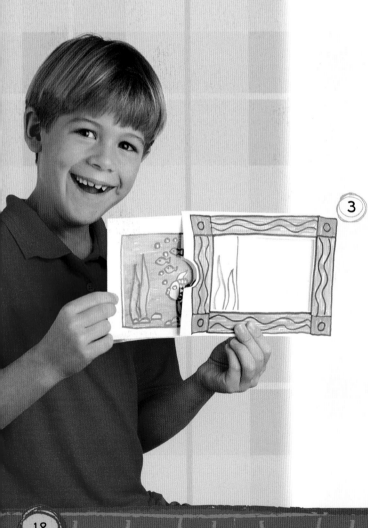

Decorate the front frame with a pattern. Cut a piece of paper the same size as one section of the card and draw on your design.

5

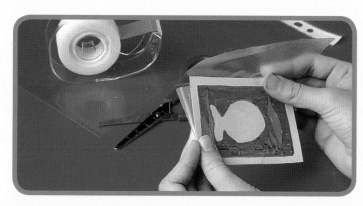

Slip your picture into the plastic folder with the top against a fold. Trim the plastic to fit the picture. Tape the back to the plastic.

6

Use a black marker to draw an outline of the picture on the plastic.

**DID YOU KNOW?**
Another word for a magician is "conjuror." Both perform magic tricks!

Open out the card, and slip the bottom flap between your picture and the plastic layer on top. The bottom flap is now between the two. Fold the frame down over the top. Grip the plastic and paper and pull; the picture will magically appear in color as you pull it out.

# NOTEPAPER

## YOU WILL NEED

- Paper: blue, white, green
- Black marker
- Scissors
- White glue
- Hole punch

 1

Decorate the blue sheet of paper first. Draw, then cut out, small fluffy white clouds and glue them onto the sky.

2

Decide how low the skyline will be, then draw and cut a wavy line across the top of a sheet of green paper to make hills. Glue the green paper on top of the blue to create a scene.

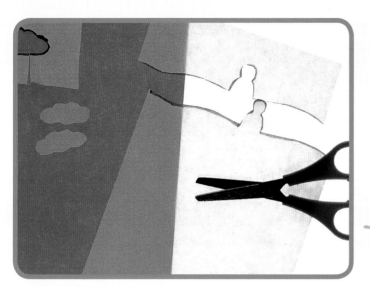

Make a snow scene decorated with a cheerful snowman. Draw a snowman on a white sheet of paper. Remember to draw the horizon, too. Use scissors to cut out the snowman and horizon, then glue the sheet of white paper onto the blue sky.

4
KIDS

Decorate the snowman using a black marker to make his face. Use a hole punch to make lots of tiny white circles for snowflakes, then stick them on your snowy scene.

DID YOU KNOW?
Most stamps are square-shaped or rectangular, but some are shaped like circles.

# POP-UP CARDS

## YOU WILL NEED

- Colored thin cardboard
- Scissors
- Ruler
- White glue
- Colored paper
- Colored markers

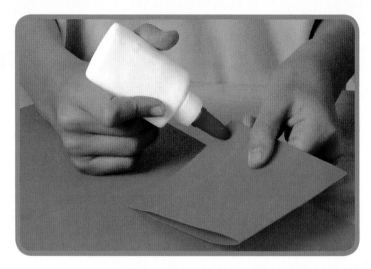

1

Fold a sheet of cardboard in half, then open it out. Now cut a smaller rectangle and fold in half. Fold a lip along the two shorter edges and glue them to the inside of the larger card to make the vase. Check the vase flattens when the card is shut.

2

Cut stems and leaves out of green paper, and glue them inside the vase. Cut out some paper flowers and glue them onto the stems, making sure they are hidden when the card is closed.

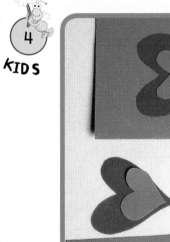

Cut lots of small hearts from folded red paper to decorate the vase.

4
KIDS

Decorate the front of the card with a large paper heart, then glue a smaller one in a contrasting color in the middle. Now you are ready to write your message inside the card.

# ENVELOPES

## YOU WILL NEED

- Occasion card: birthday, holidays, Valentine
- Colored paper
- Scissors
- Glue
- Colored markers

**1 KIDS**

Place your card in the center of the paper. Fold up the bottom of the sheet to cover the card completely. Leave an inch at the top, and $\frac{1}{2}$ inch on each side.

**2 KIDS**

Fold the top flap down, over the card.

**3**

Open out the paper completely and fold in the sides over the card. Make sure the card fits easily the folded shape.

4

Trim the excess paper from the sides of the front flap using the folds to guide you. This will make it easier to close your envelope.

5

Cut in at angles on either side of the top flap to shape it.

6

KIDS

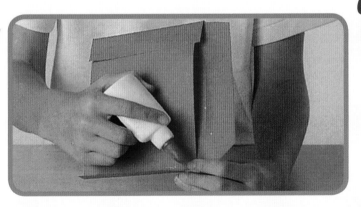

Use glue to hold the envelope's shape.

DID YOU KNOW?
Zip codes are numbers after your address that help the Post Office deliver mail to the right house or building.

Elmo likes to decorate the envelope with markers or crayons.

# FABRIC PRINTING

**YOU WILL NEED**

- Carrot, medium potato, apple
- Knife
- Kitchen towel
- Sponge
- Fabric paint: various colors
- Plain fabric
- Cookie cutters

①

Cut a carrot in half, longways. Use the sponge to spread a little fabric paint onto the flat side of the carrot.

② **KIDS**

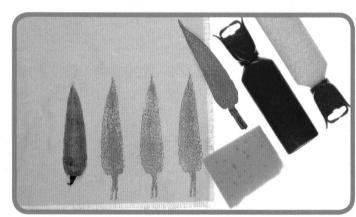

Gently press the carrot down onto the fabric. Do not move it about, or the paint will smudge. Print a row of carrots. Leave the printed fabric in a safe place to dry. Follow the directions that come with the fabric paint to set the dye.

③

Cut a potato in half. Press the cookie cutter firmly into the potato and cut away the potato around the outside. Remove the cutter, and pat the stamp dry with a kitchen towel, so it's ready for printing.

**4**

**KIDS**

Use a sponge to apply fabric paint to the stamp. Print your pattern.

**5**

Cut an apple in half and pat it dry with a kitchen towel.

**6**

**KIDS**

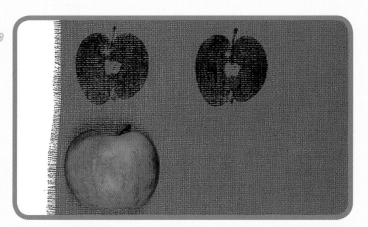

Use the sponge to apply fabric paint to the apple surface and press it down firmly onto the fabric.

**DID YOU KNOW?** Carrots grow underground. They are called root vegetables, because the part we eat is actually a root.

Cut up the fabric into rectangles and print on them, to make place mats or napkins for all your family.

# ORIGAMI BOX

## YOU WILL NEED

- Gift wrap and patterned paper in a selection of colors and weights
- Scissors

**1**
**KIDS**

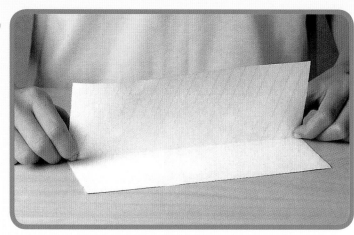

Fold a rectangle of paper in half lengthwise.

**2**
**KIDS**

Fold each half into the middle so you have 4 equal sections.

**3**

Make a narrow fold outward from both long edges.

4

Fold in the corners and tuck them under the small fold.

5

Place your fingers in the corners and carefully open out the box into shape. Use your fingers to make folds at the four corners.

DID YOU KNOW? To make a real origami model, you don't need scissors or glue—just paper to fold.

## YOU WILL NEED

- Corrugated cardboard from a grocery box
- Ruler
- Pencil
- Scissors
- Adhesive tape
- Old newspaper
- White glue
- Acrylic paint
- Paintbrushes
- Tissue paper

①

Measure and cut out two squares the same size for the box base and lid. Then measure four small rectangles for the box sides. Their longest edge should be slightly shorter than the sides of the base.

②

Use tape or glue to hold the box together. Use the top of the box to help you draw a small square to stick on the inside of the lid. Check that the lid fits into the box.

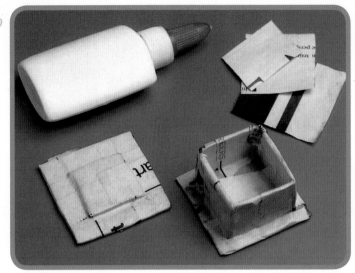

Glue two layers of newspaper squares over the box and lid. Check the lid still fits, then leave in a warm airy place to dry.

Scrunch up tissue paper and put it inside your box, before you put trinkets in it.

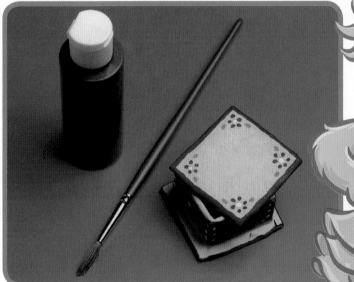

When the newspaper is dry, paint a base coat of color. You may need to paint a second coat to cover them completely. When dry, decorate the box and lid any way you wish.

# INDEX

AaBbCcDdEeFfGg